Neil Chapman is an
explores visuality in
orative methods. He
aesthetics.

Diagrams for Seriality is typset in Fleischmann,
digitised by the Dutch Type Library.

DIAGRAMS FOR SERIALITY

Neil Chapman

Copy Press

The Copy Press Limited
51 South Street
Ventnor
Isle of Wight
PO38 1NG

copypress.co.uk

Commune no. 7
Editor: Yve Lomax
Reader: Claire Smithson
Copy-editor: Sara Peacock
Design: Amerang & Dominik Junker

Front cover © Neil Chapman

Printed on Munken Print White
no.18 80gsm. Munken Print White
standard products are fsctm
and PEFC certified.
Printed and bound in England.

First edition © Copy Press Ltd/
Neil Chapman, 2014

Neil Chapman asserts the moral right
to be identified as the author of
this work.

A catalogue record for this book is
available from the British Library

ISBN-13   978-1-909570-00-9

A thought was forming like a piece of sculpture behind the eyes.

> William Golding,
> *Pincher Martin*

WITH IMPORTANT MATTERS unresolved we went to visit Martin, who was in his room as we had expected. We took the opportunity to stop for a while and to engage him in conversation. Standing, speaking, we altered our posture and gestures, doing so for comfort and at the same time to provide signals aiding our meaning and our listening. We shifted our weight from one foot to the other, placed a hand on a hip, folded our arms and unfolded them as if to mimic and then to distinguish ourselves, one from the other, just as our views might be distinguished. We turned this way and that. If we looked around Martin's room it cannot be said that we noted consciously all we saw. For the most part our eyes were drawn to the window, to the far distance, our focus lengthening on the white sky as Martin spoke and we spoke in turn.

We came by way of the old road, which we enjoy, with its concrete poles spaced to mark a division for pedestrians. But something had come to spoil the conversation. Approaching the new buildings I had begun to comment, to do so in a way unremarkable enough, it seemed to me, merely describing recent thoughts and anticipating my colleague's comments in return. I was speaking and had not yet indicated that it was her moment to reply. When that moment came she spoke and did so in a polite way. All the same it was apparent that a division had appeared, her courteousness no small part in its demarcation.

So when we arrived at Martin's our company was under some strain. I for my part felt stunned, she surely felt the same, as if two bodies had been knocked against one another then sent spinning in other directions. We did our best to conceal it, in fact did not discuss the matter until later when I read her passages on the museum and saw that she had drawn something from what happened to frame her story. It is set in exhibition halls, the kind one might visit in company, which, due to their vast size and echoey silence, are apt to instil feelings of isolation. These sentiments she evokes well, doing so through descriptions both of the interiors and of the protagonists who move there. Their plaintive dialogue is a prism by which the vast and silent interiors seem to become more vast and more silent still. In her story there is a reconciliation, but only after those described have made their exit and taken time to discuss the visit and the works they encountered that day.

The protagonists try to reconstruct the route they took through networks of galleries, to bring to mind again the pictures and artefacts they saw. When their attempt fails it does so in a peculiar way. On one wall in particular, they remember, something was displayed. They cannot recall what. With growing curiosity, though they can no longer name it, they note the size and dimensions of that thing becoming more certain in their recollection while in every other respect its identity slips away further. The two agree: they cannot rid themselves of a troubling suspicion that the hole in their memory is not their own shortcoming. In a way that cannot quite be accounted for, the wall-mounted work itself is responsible. They see the place in which it was but see it obscured as if burnt out from its centre, nothing but a rough margin remaining.

A familiar image thus comes to aid her story, that of a frame of celluloid shown melting as the projector's claws fail to catch. Film-makers reflecting on the mechanics of cinema enjoy showing the same moment of malfunction – moving image reduced to erratic jumps, frame stilled for an instant then warped, discoloured, liquidated. It is a sequence giving pause for thought due to its infinite regress: will this the representation of the mechanism for representation malfunction too?

Having identified the gap in their remembered journey, her protagonists find it difficult to resist thinking the matter over again. Before long they become tired and ask if it might not be better just to go back to the museum and look. It would be easy enough to do so. On reflection they decide against it. Instead, they consider that it might be possible to come to terms with their forgetfulness. As they fix their mind's eye once more on the space, their earlier feelings of irritation subside. Those same troubled sensations, which before had seemed a defining predicament, now are controlled. While they have not been banished completely they are contained, localised, a discomfort in the limbs. And that's the point at which the story ends.

An attentive reader will notice some equivocation in the way the scenario is set. The interiors through which her characters walk are named in different ways. It is, it seems, done strategically so that the story can be situated more effectively by different readers in accordance with their experiences of such places. The same intention is surely behind the author's somewhat vague invocation of various kinds of things housed in these so-called exhibition halls. There are pictures and artefacts. The whole mechanism of their display persuades a viewer to understand the resources available only when he or she goes to look. The reality is more complex: that's what the story seems to be saying.

Though the story focuses on the case of a picture, the question arises quite naturally as to how the same set of ideas might extend to other categories. The shape and volume of a thing, it might be said, is such that it seems to hide its secret. Even if it is a vessel able to be opened and peered into – perhaps *especially* if it is a vessel – the act of looking does not resolve the puzzle of mystery receding. The curiosity has been noted already that the film-maker revels in the thought that a frame of celluloid can be shown in the very process of its picture disappearing. In a way not dissimilar, where the apprehension of an artefact is concerned, a corresponding enjoyment comes in the description of its hidden interior as dark. We hear of a darkness inside bodies, a core of darkness, the darkness of matter and so on. The enjoyment of these phrases is accompanied by an irksome feeling that the terms available do not quite get a hold on what's sought.

MARTIN'S DOOR HAD BEEN open. We had walked in, giving a knock as a token as we did so. Then we were intrigued to see he had company, a woman with a broad face, eyes like buttons. She was sitting on a low stool. Martin was standing. We chose a place to stand, doing so as best we could to find the correct place while allowing ourselves a little room to adjust. The woman had arrived only a little earlier, we guessed; like us, having taken the open door if not as an invitation then as an indication that Martin was happy to have company.

Introductions were made – introductions of a kind. For instance we did not learn from Martin the name of the woman with the broad face, deducing instead that he thought we must know already. We did not give our own names, although thinking back now admit there to have been no good reason and that it might have been better to do so. Instead, being unsure of ourselves we spoke in a way to blur the matter. Where clear introductions could have been made we presented non sequiturs like paths in random directions in the hope that a way of speaking might be found. The woman with the broad face took her part. She did so either in agreement that the misdirection was necessary, or through being disorientated, or to admit that if such disorientations were necessary for us then she would take her part.

More recently some vindication has been found for those actions of our own that perplexed us a little when we found ourselves introducing confusion into conversation. We realise they may have been conditioned by other parties more profoundly than we thought. Speaking to the assistant at the bookshop we have learned that he had dealings with a woman of the same description.

The shop assistant told of the puzzlement he felt at his own actions in exchange with this customer. He had the sense that the two of them had met before. Although the woman made no acknowledgement, there were signals, he said, that his unsure recognition was mutual. He described the manner of her arrival. She seemed to know what she was looking for. A shop assistant becomes sensitive to such things, he informed us. Although lingering for a moment, pausing to look at items on display, she had the demeanour of one disguising a mission. He had seen such behaviour before and recognised in this customer a person concerned, first, not to advertise her single-mindedness. In fact she knew quite well, he said, what it was she wanted and that when she left the shop she would have purchased that thing and no other.

He put the point emphatically. There are few things that make a customer stand out more effectively than the signs of resolve, a direct line taken to a particular shelf, a lack of hesitation before retrieving an item and bringing it to the counter. Those who treat the bookshop this way miss the opportunity it provides. Even more than other kinds of shop, he remarked, bookshops are places to forget plans and schedules, to indulge instead in reverie. Those who walk past shelves of books without being drawn in other directions only indicate they may lack the thoughtfulness required to read the very books they are so intent on buying.

All the same, the shop assistant admitted, on this occasion his assessment of the customer in question was clouded by the idea already mentioned that he and she may not have been complete strangers to one another. On reflection he was not at all sure that her manner was of one disguising single-mindedness. Perhaps it was her response to the same uncertainty he was feeling.

It was for our benefit that the shop assistant went into these things in some detail, testifying to having learnt something about himself in the process. We will want to make a related observation about the exchange we had with Martin involving the woman with the broad face. But first our conversation with the shop assistant helps by providing evidence to further an intuition. Names and descriptions are not the only tools where identification is concerned. Effects altogether less tangible contribute. They emerge in the event of an encounter. As they are resistant to our apprehension, so they do not respect the usual demarcations of bodies. Consequently, for those caught up in such encounters, the demarcations of bodies become less certain. Then they act in a contrary way to induce puzzlement as to the origin of actions. A person feels uncertain if he or she is acting or being acted upon.

WE HAVE BEEN FORTUNATE recently to find ourselves confidants of a notable colleague, who has been generous and spoken in an unguarded way about events of his childhood. In the classroom, activities were in place to keep him and his classmates busy. At the same time he was busy with an activity of his own, one more or less obscured by his apparent obedience. These things have become significant for him only much later as he remembers how his mind was occupied by something entirely different from what the teacher had intended.

In describing his account this way we are making inferences and so risking that we may misrepresent what he has said. Furthermore, we would want to resist stating the analysis that may seem clear enough all the same. The dots should not be joined. That said, it does not mean we are left without a role in these matters. If the potential of what he has recounted can be emphasised in a way that respects his mode of speaking, then perhaps he will be led to see it in a way that would not have been possible otherwise.

At the same time it would be foolish not to

point to a fact that appears as a problem to the great constituency of his readers: no new book is forthcoming. He may feel some responsibility in this regard; he has not said. But a certain vividness in his remarks in question suggests that something is happening to alter the current condition of his work, which those whose professional business it is to comment on such things call the writer's silence.

It is appropriate to speak this way, perhaps for unexpected reasons, in terms of the joining of dots. The events of which our friend has spoken involve drawing, the repeated inscription of an emblem found on the pages of a book, a type-setter's ornamental mark, a curlicue separating sequences of paragraphs across a number of pages. He saw it with peculiar clarity while the story was being read. He felt compelled to copy the emblem. When he realised his facility to do so he went on to draw it again, thus establishing a procedure.

We will tell the story as he has told it and do so more fully in due course. First, it has not escaped our attention that an equation can be made between this notable colleague and Martin, whose work in many respects we see the same way. Martin too has invented a procedure – indeed, one involving drawing – and there is no question he works equally single-mindedly. Furthermore he employs related processes of repetition, which are bound intimately (and paradoxically) to his imperatives for invention.

We bring the two cases up together because the equation presents itself as an idea now; we do so despite the complications that will ensue.

It is our view that the order of thought itself contains resources most often systematically devalued. Certainly clarity must be pursued in revision, but not in a way insensitive to the emergent difficulty in which clarity of another order can be found.

In a different way this point – our insistence that unusual attention be paid to the turbulence of emerging ideas – has been made already. The potential of a story resides in large part in its meaning not being stated. It is well known. Such resolve to hold off from giving the analysis, of making the conclusion, is an insight had in the middle of things. Something resistant to being named is taking place. To linger in spite of what the story-form demands may be judged idiosyncratic. So be it. The more subtle and complex conclusion is always to be found in the wrong place.

WE WILL SPEAK AT SOME length about Martin, about the single-minded procedures of his work that employ repetitive strategies and operations of not looking – these latter all the more surprising given his work with images. At the same time it has to be noted that when we walked into his room that day a different work drew our attention first, a large panel by the window. Martin had painted his name.

In a way not at all usual of proper names, Martin's name contains a prediction of his destiny. He was fond of telling us. When we changed our plan that day and dropped in on him unannounced he took the opportunity to tell us again. In any case if he had not we would have had reason to bring it up ourselves because of the large canvas by the window on which he had written his name impressively, colouring the letters and using two colours. Those letters in the middle of the name assumed prominence in red with a gold outline. So the name was presented as if it had three levels, two on either side constituted by its first letter and by its last two letters, the third level in the middle. Thus the name was like a podium and Martin's inscription of it an act of stepping to the top.

Then again, to describe the name thus is only a portion of what might be said. A mechanism in reading causes such sequences of letters within words, which can be read otherwise as words in themselves, to be hidden. Indeed, there is a mechanism of reading that hides the divisions between letters, so that when we do notice – for instance, by an accidental kind of looking that sees the gaps as material and as positive shapes – they appear as decisive as had asterisks been placed there.

Such experiences attract the attention of those with an interest in eye-brain function, who will want to account for the proximity and mutual exclusivity of ways of seeing. Without a background in that field, I have found my own encounter with the puzzle of alternate ways of looking come in a different and more troubling way. It has been in relation to opinions. These are ways of seeing too. With reflection on the troubling and unexpected disagreement that appeared when my colleague and I were making our way towards Martin's, it seems she took issue with precisely this point, although for reasons of her own did not say so directly.

Even now these matters are not clear. I give the account as best I can to indicate the sequence in which things took place. I had assumed my opinions to be stable, my mind made up to all intents and purposes on all the important issues that might come up in conversation. On that basis, I had assumed, confidence could be had. Then it had occurred to me that there might be something to be gained in being less certain – more specifically in being seen to question the assumption of self-confidence. To be clear, this was all to a large extent a matter of performance. I had rehearsed, had imagined how the idea would be put and the response it would provoke. That response, needless to say, was one favourable to my own interests just as expressions of self-reflexive uncertainty are bound to elicit respect.

We were talking as we walked, which is to say I was giving my account and she was listening as we made our way past the old buildings, the concrete pillars by the roadside marking our transit as we passed. I had prepared my idea and had thought through the different ways it might be said. I had not spoken it out loud but had rehearsed quietly, anticipating the moment I would have the chance to voice the thought. I had practised with different wordings. My colleague understands such ambulatory processes. She uses them herself to work on her narratives. In not being written, such compositions made during the process of walking are subject to the turbulent flows that appear around the edges of thought – subject even to great surges of thought that render what had been stories no more than counter-currents.

My colleague and I have observed our notable

friend walking. He has been seen gesturing in a manner to indicate that he too is engaged in the composition of narratives with imaginary characters. It has crossed our mind to ask if he is conscious of what he is doing. Furthermore, does he consider it work when he leaves his place of work to walk without a destination in mind, for the ameliorating effects that such journeys surely bring? In a continued effort not to provide him with unsanctioned advice we, ourselves, propose The Parable of Errands.

THE WORKING DAY TAKES on a strange form. From a certain perspective it is hardly recognisable as such. It becomes in its entirety a sequence of transits: first the trip from home to place of work, then in the middle of the day from place of work to home, then to and from other places in order to carry out errands. Pause to feel the impact of the term. What material need do they satisfy? Since none, they are errands only in a special sense, controlled by something other than the immediate needs of work. The other business of work and the economy of work are reduced to near zero between trips made for reasons obscured.

All the same, all takes place within the schedule of a working day. What the 'all' consists of here is precisely the question. If the so-called working day remains well illuminated as such, its internal components are not quite so discernible.

This is to say that activities of the errand take place beneath the cover of a certain kind of normality. The paradox can be expressed in its sharper form as a series of questions: *What working day is it that works as cover for work? What work hollows a space at its own heart, a mysterious cavity in which another work might reside? Will that other work not retreat once more to hollow a space of its own?*

In its next step the parable proposes a subtle but important alteration of terms so that it does not have to rely on ideas of hollowed spaces, dark or mysterious cavities. The aim may be to win back the forms of work aided by the walking away from, or walking at a tangent to, the day's proper business. If so, it will not necessarily be achieved through exposure. That said, it is the business of parables that something be exposed. So the proviso is given that the scenes to follow maintain their distance from characters and, consequently, their passivity within the broader trajectory of thought.

You walk the length of a pale concrete road, without reaching its end feel the aura of destinations. Then consider the road's rough edges, broken despite its construction designed for resilience. There are sections, one partition of pale concrete separated from the next by a cushion of tar so that in the heat and in the cold the concrete will not crack. The pale road peters out. Here might be a place to stop, to wait. There is a bollard, small obelisk of cement heavy with aggregate of pebbles, round and smooth, water-sorted, alike in size, various in colour; on the top an iron ring to take a chain directing pedestrians and other traffic.

Having time to look, notice this place is governed by competing regimes. There is an old architecture and a new architecture. Each has its own administration, the first with remit to conserve, the second with a programme to develop. Communication takes place between the two only when it is necessary. Then decisions are made to establish where the next foundations will be dug, which of the old buildings will be maintained and which allowed to fall into disrepair. Building projects are halted part-way so that it becomes unclear to which regimes they belong.

In due course you can orientate yourself differently – in relation to the bollard, for instance, stand with a foot against it making use of the angles of its top surface. Then it is good to look closer, to crouch low and place a hand on its flat side. There feel the smoothness of pebbles. Consider their qualities. Test to see if with a little effort one round pebble might be loosened. Risking rebuke, children have done the same and been told to curtail their explorations. You may look up when you think of it and imagine that, from the cloudy darkness of windows nearby, people watch. Not being seen they derive pleasure from it, but no more than you, who cannot see them, derive pleasure from the thought they may be watching.

If their observations are surreptitious, these people behind dark windows look on with vacant minds. You know as much because your own mind is emptied by the thought of them looking. Then the windows themselves come to appear like eyes, façades like faces. From the cloudy vacancy of a building's eyes watchers get their vacant thoughts, a pleasure in their watching to speculate why people stop and wait in a place not usual for it, down by the bollard, where the pale concrete road comes to an end.

WE HAD BEEN LOOKING at Martin's name displayed in red and gold before our attention turned to other work, a body of work sitting as a stack of panels with their faces to the wall. In addition there was one panel on the stand. Its composition was organised to show something, a common thing rendered with care against a dark background. Although we saw, we do not remember what. Martin was, he explained, taking the panels as they were finished and stacking them.

When he did so he would not look at them again. There was a pallet – actually no more than a scrap of board – onto which were squeezed colours in a limited range: Lamp Black, Payne's Grey, Titanium White, Raw Umber. There were rags on the floor like bandages. He had used them to wipe his hands. Looking at these things in turn we fancied we gathered something of what was hidden on the panels turned away.

Martin would come to the room every day, he reminded us; the panels took time and he spent his time that way, working and adding to the work stacked against the wall so that it measured his time, the stack as deep as the time was long.

My colleague's writing on the exhibition halls has been aided by our visits to speak to Martin. She has found inspiration in other places too, through events in which she has been implicated and in the work of other colleagues. One eminent colleague in particular has been helpful. She has read his work and watched him speaking on ideas related to her own. Seeing in his work the facility that a thinker can develop, the way an inquiry can extend its scope, she has extended the scope of her own writing. She has shifted the focus of her attention from viewers in exhibition space to the painter, specifically that curious moment when a painter becomes dispassionate observer of his own canvas.

A man with unkempt appearance is described slumped on a chair in front of work propped against the opposite wall. Though in this fictional treatment she leaves it unsaid, the reader will infer it to be Le Douanier Rousseau. If he appears to be in a state of inactivity, it is not in any simple sense. While his body reclines and indicates every resource sapped, the very collapse is liberating an intensity of work just now taking place. In a moment, defying the exhaustion of his repose, he will leap to his feet and take up the tools of his craft. His alteration to the work will not fail to prove his genius. Then finding himself overcome with anxiety the painter will pack his things to leave.

An interview has been recorded in which

our esteemed colleague speaks to a journalist about Rousseau's *Surprised! Tiger in a Tropical Storm*. He describes a moment in front of the picture in which his assumed status as viewer was altered. His role and that of the painter swapped places – or that, he says, is how it seems.

It is funny to see the interviewee and the journalist pacing slowly and purposefully in step as they talk, both men with their hands clasped firmly behind their backs. They are talking of things if not difficult to articulate then tricky enough to identify in the first place – trickier still to keep as the topic of conversation without more ordinary ideas coming stealthily to depose them. While it cannot be doubted that the two are engaged in important discussion, in some respects they are performing their thinking and thus adding an insurance against distraction. After all, the tape is rolling and the opportunities not unlimited for getting to the crux of their issues.

So it might be said there are those, like my colleague's esteemed colleague, who have the facility to juggle what others cannot hold simultaneously, which is to say thought and its performance. That facility is a peculiar confidence. For others, thinking precipitates a contrary effect of instilling doubt in their minds. Becoming unsure they choose not to speak. All the same their thought need not be lost. A collective effort can be initiated. It takes a peculiar skill, no doubt, but if thinking can be witnessed in its happening then, through representations, it can be relayed.

Shortly a case will be presented. A person will

be described on all fours, on a great pile of papers, looking intently, reading. There is insufficient light. It is uncomfortable. These papers, which have landed accidentally, should be treated with more care than can be afforded by one whose whole weight rests on them. A theme will be developed regarding the contents of the page that grip his attention and about the reasons they should do so. But first, the point will be made that there is a great wealth in the most often unperceived articulations of a body in the moment of being gripped: what such gestures have to say and what they show.

For the person to have settled – in both the physical and volitional sense – on this carpet of disorder is a wrestling with discomfort. A strange power of awkwardness is tapped, made into a resource for the faculty of attention to drive it with new vigour. A hand, which the person places to support his weight and so better facilitate his downwards gaze, feels the surface in contact. It is intimacy of the kind between opponents in combat.

MUCH IS TO BE SAID FOR a relaxed attitude towards one's employees, the shop assistant remarked, especially so when they are young. At least as far as it is possible, proprietors should let the young find their own way through a day's work. A business allows that some inefficiency can be absorbed. In the meantime, if in unsanctioned

ways, the young are training themselves. The bene-
fits will not be recuperated immediately – when they
are, perhaps only by a different employer. In that
respect even businesses in competition might work
together for a common good.

He was not aware of the precise work being
done by his young helper, who had been in the store-
room at the back for some time now. Things were
quiet in the shop. In the meantime one customer
had been attracting his attention. From his position
behind the till he was assessing her behaviour. She
had cast a stealthy glance in his direction as she
stood looking with interest – or pretending to – at
items on display. He watched through a gap in the
shelving as she made her way to a different section,
where she selected a volume then stood for a moment,
not opening it but holding the book in her grip, in
both hands.

Although he could not remember the circumstances in which they had met, there was no
question he recognised her. He could see the partition
of his own life with which she was associated. The
intuition was underscored by her choice of book,
largely comprising illustrations: a resource for someone involved in an image-inquiry, perhaps? Such
research requires that images from diverse sources
be placed in relation to one another. Handling
images in this way teaches the researcher sensitivity
to the complex and multiple capacities that images
have for setting up alliances, one with another.
Images establish their incommensurability too,
so that where continuity had been assumed,

unbridgeable divisions appear; placement becomes displacement, and so on. All these tendencies have to be seen and studied. Work with images requires that archives are built. Plan chests and filing cabinets are needed in which images can be collected in their various material forms, photographic prints, magazine cuttings, slides of the old-fashioned kind, in order to multiply the possible encounters and so to witness the greater variety of impacts that one can have on another placed in proximity.

The woman approached the till. Now the shop assistant hoped to satisfy his curiosity. As he engaged her in conversation in a stealthy way he might be able to glean what he needed to work out who she was. These were the intentions on his mind as she handed him the book. He described to us in some detail how he took it and how he took the opportunity, perhaps unusually, to open the volume himself and to remark. Book-sellers will do so as a matter of course to find the price (pencilled first page, top right-hand corner) but this was something more presumptuous. Conscious of it, he was aware of being scrutinised, his manner measured with what seemed to him peculiar acumen. He was apt to get a little confused, he confessed. Turbulence entered into his thought. On the other hand his wits were about him sufficiently that he understood it unwise to attempt any correction of the words that were coming out wrongly.

Thus his own unwieldy expression allowed the shop assistant to appreciate a distinction between, on the one hand, a speaking self and, on the other, a self listening while the same speaking is taking place.

Instances of comparable utterances make themselves available. We take the case of a writer whose early work has achieved unexpected notoriety. A book of that sort will be given a prominent place, a stand of its own at eye level in the bookshop where browsing customers will be drawn to it more surely. It is an early edition of our notable friend's slim volume. His success is to have rid his writing of all unwieldy expression. The achievement has been called miraculous synthesis – one that will be difficult for a young writer to follow.

Questions of responsibility are different in each case. For the shop assistant, the producer of unwieldy speech, it is to acknowledge a level of ownership, to continue to resist the impulse for mere correction and to find composure in the proximity of utterances that have come out wrongly. Such composure amounts to an embracing of distraction. For the prodigious young writer the responsibility will be to follow up and to supersede the early success. If it is not clear to him how he should do so there will be difficult years, years of darkness. But let's remember that darkness attributed this way only compounds the problem. It takes what's already hidden and then hides it once more.

As the Parable of Errands is developed the point will be made clear. Think it through again. A clandestine form of work seemed to be hidden within work in other respects organised in the normal way. Such structures risk an infinite regress: 'Will that other work (a work within work) not retreat once more to hollow a space of its own?' So a subtle and important alteration of terms is needed to replace the cover of darkness with an idea of distraction – or better still, of decoy. If these two terms – cover and decoy – are not wholly distinct, the revision does its work all the same. As the utterance coming out wrongly is judged abnormal the decoy is in place. And what is it that a decoy does? It attracts others of its own appearance to draw nearer. In this way the parable shows how the errands work. It is not that they hide one form of work within another. Rather, they draw unusual forms of normality into proximity. Then as normality is one in a family of terms along with banality, the everyday, habit and so on, these others will have their shy cousins coaxed nearer.

THE WOMAN WITH THE broad face had been quiet but now had something to say. We listened and were given to understand that she liked the stack of panels propped against the wall in Martin's room, which he was adding to every day. With her remark we were drawn to consider it more closely and to agree. Quite apart from what each one might show, the stack of panels was a thing worthy of attention. She was paying a compliment. Martin remained quiet, listening while she did so.

We remember her composure, how she sat,

the sense of satisfaction that came into her words, the relish with which she spoke them, measuring their gravity. And we watched Martin, if not thinking to gauge his response, doing so in any case until we saw his listening to be like a void opening. He listened to the compliment being paid and it was as if his head was emptied all the better to listen. The expression on his face made it evident. We anticipated that would change, and it did. When he prepared to speak, his expression changed to indicate his head no longer emptied.

Furthermore, Martin's listening was like his whole body turned to listening and made a listening-instrument, all that has been said of the head being true of the body and the head together. Both were vacated. Then they were filled as listening was brought to an end and speaking or readiness for speaking resumed.

Had we not known Martin better we might have read his appearance then as indicating a dysfunction of the brain. We now understand such appearances when we see them elsewhere on the contrary as signs of a peculiar intelligence. Take our notable friend. We have no image of him as a child, at least none except that gleaned from his story. At the same time we think it no affront to the story-teller's art, nor to the good listener's facility, to bring to bear insights gathered elsewhere and to develop a story's images in whatever way we can. And so it is a child with just such an expression that we think of now.

In a primary school class on an ordinary day

in February he was handed a book. Now he is unable to recall the story (a traveller, a donkey, an Austrian landscape in winter?) remembering only one page, its layout, the curves of an old-fashioned typeface, the smell of the paper. The story was organised on the page in sequences of paragraphs each separated from the next by a tiny emblem of fine and intricate design. While taking the place of words the little curling mark did not mean anything, at least not in the way words do. Nor did it represent any thing as pictures do. And yet it directed reading. It compelled his attention. Neglecting the proper business of the morning he copied its shape and drew it between sums. He used it to separate sentences, placed the emblem alternately with items on a list until with some puzzlement the teacher addressed him on the matter. Even as he anticipated her rebuke he could see that what he had done was odd. And it was odd not to have been more aware of it until having it pointed out.

A child embraces activities with enthusiasm. If to do so is more than play, then it is work and play woven together. To have noticed the emblem, to have learned its shape, to have repeated the drawing, to have made the inscription and to have done so at every opportunity until directed otherwise: these parts assemble into a practical whole. In its own way it was an inquiry, one anticipating the later inquiry of his adult work. If it is true to say that the work is literature, calling it such is to classify it in a way insensitive to its origin, so that even he will forget the place from which it came.

Through all that must surely have changed there is a continuity of procedure undertaken with single-minded resolve. Perhaps a new name is needed – one to replace the name of literature, to challenge all forms of thought that miss the continuity here discovered. The name will invoke the questions asked by those whose inquiries work by joining together elements otherwise seen as incommensurable: *What comes next? What is it for something to come next? Is there a blueprint for the sequence, a diagram for seriality?*

SO WE WERE INTERESTED in Martin's appearance as he listened and no less in the gestures of the woman with the broad face. We were interested in what was being said and in the silences between words, which made the gestures more apparent. Like Martin, the woman made her whole body an instrument, in her case first for speaking. Her words were odd in that respect, at odds with all of what is to be expected such that words are thought to issue forth after a resolution having been made regarding meaning. As we listened and adjusted our listening to understand, we could see that in this case the order was being confounded.

We can say now that the woman with the broad face, eyes like buttons, came to appear to us that way only then. Despite all that was said, when we saw her first we had not thought to attribute descriptions. The broadness of her face and the buttons of her eyes became apparent to us as such only when she began to speak.

Something of these insights can be taken up elsewhere to address questions that have remained resistant, for instance in relation to disagreement that appears unexpectedly between colleagues. Might sudden and unaccountable evaporation of consensus be explained less in terms of what is said and more with recourse to the appearance that one interlocutor has for another? Is that the explanation for what transpires to take the different parties so by surprise?

Remember again how I explained it, while struggling to do so on account of the complexity of what had taken place. I had expressed the idea that my views were coming to change. I had done so most probably without realising the subterfuge in the remark, that it would tend to work in my interests to the extent that self-reflexivity elicits respect. I had gone a step further to say that all my view seemed subject to the same alteration. Furthermore, the shift was no less than an about-turn.

While faithful to my run-throughs, when voiced the words sounded different: odder, more questionable. As if to measure them my colleague paused, not answering but letting the words hang. And I paused with her. Although what I had said was not marked as a question it seemed to hang that way: am I coming to change my views? In every case will those that were their contraries appear more plausible? Will all my thoughts be subject to the same alteration?

Being as good as any at inferring where statements made as such are masquerading, my colleague did just that. Then she responded, replying with unexpected brevity to say she did not think so.

Certainly it is the case that words spoken and ideas expressed have the facility to provoke unexpected images of appearance. It would be a commonplace to note it: we see people differently on account of what they say. What happened here was altogether more remarkable. She looked and she saw in me precisely the person she had expected and her disappointment multiplied.

It is a more complimentary image we form of our notable friend when we see him as a child in his primary school class. No one was there to witness. It is odd to say so when the room would have been full of his young classmates. We know that a teacher was there too. She features in the story presiding over affairs. On account of the positions they hold, both pupils and the teacher are rendered systematically insensitive to what they might otherwise apprehend. Classmates are caught up in a storm of their own concerns. The cacophony of voices rules out reflection on those around them. The teacher is programmed precisely to not see; her remit is to rule out all taking place that does not conform to her programme. The witnesses, if there are any, are those privileged as confidants after the fact, those who have listened well to a story concisely told.

MY COLLEAGUE'S RESPONSE to the ideas I was trying to express was to contradict. It was the brevity of her remark that shocked me. When I explained the point I wished to make she replied simply that she did not think so. The division now appearing was irreversible. All consensus assumed to this point had been a mistake, a mere appearance disguising fundamental non-communication. We were, each of us, cast into isolation.

Remembering that feeling, my thoughts return once more to our notable friend's esteemed colleague, how he is distinguished from the other precisely by the great mass of respectful company around him. Problems relating to isolation are not missing in his reflections, only when he addresses the theme he makes evident his secure knowledge that friends are close by. The partition of his isolation may be equally profound but its walls are glass. That way his thoughts are free to race to the moment when he will tell what has happened, impressing his listeners with the great variety of his experience.

It was as a visitor in the normal sense that he had made his way into the museum. Then, on coming across Le Douanier Rousseau's *Surprised!*, he found that role altered. As he puts it with characteristic flair, 'I was the one surprised – astonished, in fact – to feel giant drops of warm rain hitting the back of my neck.'

The journalist pursues the issue, asking a question – in fact, making a statement – to say he hears in his interviewee's remarks a powerful endorsement of the painter's skill.

'Well perhaps,' comes the reply. 'It is something else too. Skill involves a certain measure of control. Here the control seemed to have escaped the painter – escaped the picture, even. If it had not become mine it certainly seemed to have been lent for a moment. The sensation of rain was one I could cause then bring to an end too. And it was with a gesture as simple as that of turning to look and turning away.'

He confesses to feeling self-conscious as he cast a surreptitious glance around in fear that he might be singled out on account of this micro-climate actualising itself above and around him in the exhibition space, which he seemed to be able to materialise and dematerialise at will. 'The event is connected to past experiences,' he explains, 'of being caught in a storm, the strangeness of foreign weather. Rousseau has painted the sky in an ominous grey. The rain is depicted in an innovative way, with diagonal marks of a milky glaze. These qualities together seemed to bring back the memory.

'Posture is part of the explanation too – my own and the tiger's. There was an unexpected correspondence. The tiger is drawn half-superimposed over the jungle flora. As one account has it, Rousseau copied his drawing from another picture then in circulation. The oddness of his painting is a result of that borrowing not being assimilated sufficiently. There is ambiguity in the animal's leaping movement. Not quite jumping forwards or backwards it seems to be jumping both ways at once. This awkward animation in combination with a representation of rain so un-equivocally directional invokes well the exuberant panic of a sudden storm, everyone running for cover.'

'What about the tiger's expression?' the interviewer asks. 'It's mentioned in the title. That's another part of how the picture works, isn't it?'

'If we gather the expression to be the tiger's fear of lightning, it is despite the composition, which buries that aspect of the narrative. The animal's shock is striking first because it seems to have no cause external to the creature. It's a kind of auto-shock. That in turn emphasises the curious omni-directionality of the tiger's leap.'

In the fictional treatment in which a painter inferred to be Le Douanier Rousseau is described sitting slumped in a chair in front of work propped against the opposite wall, the same jerky movements are attributed. Defying the exhaustion of his repose the painter leaps up from his chair to make a decisive alteration to the work. The story has him leave and describes him wandering off on some spurious errand. Then he returns. At that point the real interest emerges, when the writing addresses the loss of agency that can manifest itself in the midst of a painter's work. All the same it might be wondered if, in skipping quickly over the passage of departure, a peculiar opportunity has not been missed.

Doorways are places of transformation. A further scene can be set. Think of it this way. You have packed your things to leave. A resolution has been reached and you have spoken it to yourself in words if not vocalised then separated clearly enough one from the other. Having reached the end of your options, or having concluded on the basis of evidence that the options are ended, you tell yourself it is thus and pack to go. What's required of such departures is efficiency. A moment can be taken to ensure that the bag is packed and nothing forgotten. Then an expression of resolve must be found, a look of confidence and a posture to embed again the urgency of work.

No sooner has the threshold been crossed, no sooner has the door swung closed, than the more active imperatives of work appear once more to object that they have been too hastily judged exhausted. The doorframe is no incidental element. It works on passing bodies, in this case to bring the pointless errand into consciousness as such, if only just sufficiently. The exit operates along with an imperative of productivity. Each goads the other in the theatre which together they make, to ask in affected voices if this so-called errand will do what is asked of it or if, on the contrary, it will precipitate a decline – first of the process, then of the one who works.

A momentary hesitation in the doorway might be taken as unremarkable except that the gesture makes evident an odd and surprising quality. Seeing it, one with a view to witness will infer what you have not been able to admit to yourself. This exit is flight.

IT WAS SAID OF THE woman as she came into the bookshop that she cast her eyes around at the items on display. Her manner may have been subterfuge on account of her awareness, even as she stepped through the door, that she was being watched. She paused for a moment to pick up a volume sitting on its own on a stand at eye level, an early edition of a slim but notable work.

The book begins with a conversation between several characters who are revealed as bodiless presences located with a high view on proceedings. Their observations are scientific, albeit of a non-human kind, regarding events that confound their expectations of the species under consideration, which is to say the human species. The story then cuts to a terrestrial vantage point described through the eyes of a man who stands looking out over a placid scene. In a way that takes the reader by surprise the scene gazes back. It sees in the man a perfect mirror of its own placid manner. And the man sees the scene seeing him, and so on until he must steady himself.

Earlier, before he set out, even as he anticipated his destination he felt a familiar despondency approaching. Now the fact reappears and puts itself at the side of his route like a distance marker. However many steps it has taken him to get this far, the same number will be required to take him home. With every step forward his return journey is made longer. Still he walks. If there is no reason to continue, neither is there one to stop. Before long he reaches the harbour, where he finds himself alone. Most people have work to do and little time to walk aimlessly, he reflects. There is nothing to see – nothing of any interest. Two small birds flit into view and land on barnacle-covered steps leading to water that swells and draws back with barely a sound. He watches them peck at scraps left by fishermen before they fly off.

Sea defences of concrete behind heavy rusted iron corrugations restrict access to the beach except at one point where there is a ramp for the nearby lifeboat. With that exit in view he plots a straight line across the sand. There are obstacles: the broken branch of a tree draped in crisp black seaweed, rocks, shallow pools isolated by the receding tide. It occurs to him that despite these things perhaps he can maintain a straight path. He might do so by focusing on the distant exit, lining it up with something closer and walking to keep the nearer of the two coordinates directly between his eye and the furthest destination. To begin with, others in the vicinity will detect nothing unusual. Then, as he is seen climbing over something he could easily walk round, their curiosity will be provoked; he will be the anomaly, the agent of unusual things taking place.

His walking assumes a rhythm, the markers oscillating in relation to one another in the line of his sight as his body moves with the natural swaying of strides. This oscillation is itself a guarantee of straightness, he tells himself. As he arrives at the closer of the two he must pick another marker a little further off, a little closer to his destination. Still, with care, the continuity of a perfect line can be maintained. The procedure contradicts everything usual of walkers, whose unfolding thought and observations work directly to produce ambulatory divergences.

While the writer presents the most ordinary scene, the story's protagonist looks at the landscape and sees something threatening. He sees a face. What is the expression on that face? We are not told. As the protagonist mirrors the landscape, so we understand the landscape's face to be one that threatens in its blandness. When he makes his homeward trip, through boredom, he invents an absent-minded game in which his own expression and his awareness of it become instrumental. It is a camouflage, the method by which he will trick others into assuming him an ordinary walker on the beach. With his bland expression he induces expressions of the same kind on the faces of those who look on, or so he imagines. To the extent that he succeeds, their ordinary assumptions will follow. Consequently, when his walking does not correspond to what's expected, their surprise will be all the more pronounced.

At the other extreme, when people lose sight of themselves, when they become unaware of how they are appearing to others, those others become uncertain too. We have experienced some-thing along the same lines. Martin seemed to have departed. In one sense he was still there but in another sense no longer quite inhabiting his body – and this was the case on account solely of his expression. Then looking at him we, ourselves, began to feel a certain kind of bodiless sensation. We think it was on that occasion we looked at Martin properly for the first time. We looked closely at his features. We looked at his eyes and were sur-prised to find them appearing oddly so that they were little more than accidents on the surface of a volume – a volume no more recognisable as Martin than would have been the features in isolation. Now dare we say those features rolled a little. Not quite in the way eyes are said to roll but like it nonetheless, each that could be called a feature on his face rolling as if held in a fold of skin allowing it to do just that, to be held on the surface and at the same time to be mobile there.

Then Martin prepared to speak. As we had anticipated, his expression changed. It is difficult to say which happened first. And so we wonder if preparing to speak after having spent time listening causes a person's expression to change or if, alternatively, that preparation to speak is the effect of a change of expression. In any event as Martin spoke he did not move the conversation on. In fact his words seemed to do the opposite.

CAUSING STASIS IN CON-
versation was strategy on
Martin's part. The reasons
were easy enough to interpret, as suggested already,
it being the moment of
a compliment paid. If he
were to think back and if
he were to come across
my colleague's stories on the exhibition halls,
he might notice that she has based her writing on
him to some extent. Martin is not someone who
could be described as apt to speak incessantly and

unthinkingly in the way her character does, but in so far as that mode has a circling momentum, the same stasis results.

Then a second protagonist is presented, likewise, without being named – perhaps in a disguise under which is found the author herself. Together, these two are about to walk from the atrium into the exhibition halls. The second has anticipated how things will go this afternoon and draws back behind an impassive defence. She wishes to neutralise the flow of unnecessary words coming her way. All the same the other's desire for speaking and hers for silence are not symmetrically opposed. She has things to say too, only fears they will not be heard in all their seriousness. To offer them now would be to give thought away too freely. The other is in the wrong frame of mind. If she is correct in her judgement, if his desire to speak is rendering his capacity to listen insufficient, for his part a sensitivity to events is not diminished. He sees that conversation will not take place just yet, is unsure why but understands his best interests to be served by playing the role prescribed.

Just as he looks across and thinks now that she might be amenable, his companion dictating events takes a step behind a pillar. The gesture is slight enough that it might not mean anything. She has not turned her back, she may even have shifted her orientation towards him, but now he can no longer see her face and that is enough to put doubt in his mind. So he delays a moment longer. The judgement has been good, she thinks. Conversation is stalled once more. At the same time no accusation of coldness can be levelled against her. For a moment longer she holds him at a distance so that he might think before he speaks.

Her character thus forced by the other to play a prescribed role, the writer creates a predicament with dramatic consequences. Reading it, one can feel his isolation – all the more powerfully because at root it is a story of companionship. In other circumstances role-playing is more effectively a matter of playful experimentation. Our acquaintance at the bookshop put it well when he described his amusement at the way his own identity as custodian of the books seems to impel him to follow certain patterns of behaviour. He is not averse to doing so quite purposefully from time to time, he says. It adds some interest to his day. For long stretches there is nothing much to do. He could attend to the administrative disorder multiplying in the back room – that would be the sensible course. Instead he sits in languid repose behind the counter while his few customers browse. Often they leave without making a purchase. And yet he is never entirely still. Even when not in conversation – either with a customer or his young assistant – he will imagine himself to be involved in exchanges. While the invented interlocution takes place he swings on his chair. He plays with this or that object picked up from his desk – a pencil, a paperclip. As he does so he finds a style to aid the dramatising of his thought.

Most probably he had not freed himself sufficiently from such internalised banter when the customer approached with the book she wished to buy. It's easy to forget, he said, when we find ourselves dealing with actual people again as opposed to the transitory visitors populating our inner worlds, that we do not have the same access to their thoughts, nor knowledge of their desires. Actual encounters, if it makes sense to call them that at all, when they do happen, can take us unawares. The penetrating gaze he found himself subject to during that momentary exchange was one such.

He had wanted to comment on her purchase, to do so as a way of initiating conversation. Then his mind had become overloaded with other thoughts. It had seemed to be a result of her presence there in front of him. More specifically it was her face, in which the presence was intensified. The clarity and composure he had hoped for were not available. And so before there had been time for him to consider if his remarks were appropriate, he found himself commenting on the illustrations in the book. Indeed, his thumb was on the block-end of pages – he gestured to show us how – the pages had barely begun to turn and he was already remarking on the images. As soon as he opened his mouth the words were coming out. It was, he said, as if someone else was speaking. All he could do was watch and hope that his customer was generous enough to help repair his clumsy preamble.

THE SHOP ASSISTANT spoke at some length. He spoke on matters of gesture and presented a picture of himself in the very act of speaking. That has allowed us to speak a little more ourselves about the postures of bodies and how, when they are noticed, they can seem frozen in a single frame. Thinking back on it, when we consider the constellation of bodies present in Martin's room, the woman sitting, the rest of us standing, we remember the impression we had then that Martin was standing in a pose as if to walk. As he stood he moved a little, shifting his weight from one foot to the other. We have dwelt on the impression and have done so for unexpected reasons that take us to a different day and place, although around the same time. We have been led to consider that perhaps it was Martin we saw by the railway arch.

As it happened, that day we were taking the path that curves in a wide arc. First we saw the man from the west gate then as we followed the path we saw him from the other side. He did not go anywhere while we watched, or so we thought. We did not know Martin then nor had we met him, only coming to know him later. By the railway arch there is nothing and no reason for a person to stand. Likewise, by the east gate there may be little reason to stand. We stopped and stood there for a moment before leaving in order to look back, as it were, over our shoulders and to see if what had appeared to us first was in fact the case.

It is unlikely that the man saw us. We wonder if he considered the sight he presented, for instance, to someone watching from a window nearby. As it occurs to us to think of him watched in that way he becomes an element in a scene. If there were people looking down from high windows, they would be doing so surreptitiously. Likewise, watched by unseen witnesses with vacant minds, the man would be one of those whose mind is emptied by the thought of others looking. Why is he standing in such a place? What course of events brought him here? The man might reply that it has not been his choice. Sometimes places themselves do the choosing. Then again, what kind of place is this, by the railway arch? It is neither part of the old regime of architecture nor part of the new. Being under no jurisdiction it is precisely a place with no power of its own to choose. If that's the case the man can distinguish himself accordingly as one who has shown discernment. He has seen that where there is a threshold as between regimes of architecture, there more than any other place is the place to stop and to wait. Preference for one regime of buildings over another is not the principle that guides his decisions. On the contrary, as he has paused here his disinterest is evident. Now he might say with some confidence he is neither a blind advocate of newness nor sentimental for old things. Conscious of those categories as they enforce their rule, wise to the qualities that contradict broad themes of place is he. Again, if he finds value in progress and is repelled by it too, he would say the same for all they call old-fashioned in buildings and built places. With care he registers his fluctuations of agreement and disagreement under the influence of newness and oldness. Meanwhile with eyes unseeing and sensibilities muffled others plod from A to B.

The awkwardness of our posture as we looked ensured it was no more than a glance back. All the same we noticed something unexpected, which was that the man was not standing at all. He was walking. He was taking steps of the smallest kind.

We had other things to do and so did not stay to observe any further. What we had seen stayed with us – in fact came to seem more curious on account precisely of our having removed ourselves from the proximity. Some kind of distilling takes place. All that is peripheral to the interest, which may have been difficult to distinguish in the face of the sheer quantity of information a scene provides, falls away and thought can alight more effectively on the element amongst all that does not quite make sense.

The point is one that our esteemed colleague has made in his discussion of Rousseau's painting. This portion of his interview with the journalist, it becomes clear, is directed by a misapprehension. His interviewer has assumed our colleague's precise and thoughtful analyses to be a result of much time spent in front of *Surprised!* When the work keeps the viewer there on the spot, is that not incontrovertible evidence of success, he has asked. As he has done before, our colleague turns his interlocutor's assumptions on their head. It is a technique he uses for the power it has to engage listeners. Master of the counter-intuitive, he entertains by confounding those with whom he speaks. All the while his good-spirited playfulness guarantees the continued generosity of those whose ideas are being shown lacking.

'MY MEMORY OF THAT occasion is a little unclear,' the interviewee remarks, 'but I think I did not stay in the museum very long. After the unexpected sensation experienced in front of the picture I was inclined to move away. Now I think about it, maybe I didn't come to the museum that day specifically to look at the one painting. Maybe I had a different agenda which was then derailed by the encounter with Rousseau. Anyhow, in the meantime – and this is a curiosity too – I have not wanted to revisit, have even avoided looking at reproductions of the picture, which is unusually difficult in this instance of course due to the frequency of reproductions.

'A kind of caution has set in; a question presents itself now every time the picture comes up as to whether I'm ready to look again. My relationship with it has become strange. I'm pulled in two directions – a bit like the tiger, in fact. Unquestionably, there is a desire to go back, to stand in front of it, to see if what happened before can be induced again. At the same time there is anxiety that the event will not repeat. The rain may not detach itself to resituate as it did so strikingly.'

In what follows, the interviewee adds complexity to his analysis. Contrary to how it might appear, he argues, to avoid the painting has not been simply an attempt to conserve a memory of what took place the previous time. It has been tactical, a form of resistance and a critical interrogation of the event.

Then again, to characterise his analysis that way, saying that something has been added, is a mistake. More profoundly, the complexity was there from the start, present in the broad strokes of his commentary. The eminence of his thought is evident precisely in that, even with the qualification – even with the acknowledgement that ideas pull in two directions – his point does not come apart. Points made by others tend to be untidy by comparison. Though a speaker's first thoughts may be expressed with confidence, in a distinct voice, subsequent thoughts do not follow in the way assumed. Neither can they be described more generously as, for instance, quieter tonalities contained within the more dominant. The multiple voices of ideas compete. Unruly voices appear which have no concern except to assert their own interests. And the chatter goes on even behind the thinker's back. These thoughts left sitting are still at work cementing relationships with their neighbours, undoing alliances with others. A new round of work must be commenced to reinstate the order, to establish which voice should have authority and which others must be impelled to remain second. In certain rare circumstances, perhaps, when their simultaneity is deemed musical, the voices of ideas may speak effectively together. But as a rule, a voice within a voice must be carefully separated out and either silenced or given its own time and place to speak.

Likewise, in work adjourned correctly by those who know how to do so, moderation is achieved. The natural unruliness is allowed to persist. It is stilled. While they do not move, the ambulatory tendencies of all thoughts are noted. A record is taken of the way each may be inclined to go, which of each thought's neighbours distract it most persistently and which others have a calming effect. Their cacophonic chatter curtailed, ideas fall into peaceful co-relations.

Moderating the cacophony of voices is precisely Le Douanier Rousseau's intention as he leaves. Before he is pictured at his destination there is a whole world to be explored in the passage of his departure. In the space of a doorway important things take place. A body undergoes transformation. However, if it appears that the writer has missed a potential of her own scenario, it is wise to acknowledge that, where stories are being constructed, the writing itself may need to be pacified. There can be good reasons for sacrificing the potential in a scenario. Furthermore, if the passivity of certain passages is such that it allows a reader's mind to wander, it will be no sacrifice at all.

THE PROTAGONIST WALKS.
Before long he arrives at the high path on the north side of the park where there is a view down to the railway viaduct. For all it helps him to have left the close proximity of his work, increasingly, even this moment is governed by the labour to which he must return. As he steps back through the door his eye is drawn to a mark on the wall. He has noticed it before but never thought to consider where it might have come from. With realisation approaching fascination he deduces it to be a stain where his head rests habitually as he sits contemplating the picture propped against the opposite wall.

Le Douanier Rousseau should wash. On the other hand, if his standards of cleanliness were higher he would have missed this insight. The stain is an index of his time spent during the day, his muscles overtaken by inertia, as he stares and tries to understand the work to which his slow string of decisions is giving birth. Seen from this angle, as a sum of the gentle contacts between head and wall, the mark draws attention to the distance from normal life this work has required him to come. The origin of all that goes wrong in painting, he thinks to himself, can be traced back to the same moment when the painter leaves the pristine world of contemplation and takes up the crude tools of his craft. Then again, there is the fever of the activity, the intuitive, animated madness that expands every atom of his torso until the sun's radiation might pass through unimpeded. He finds the energy to stand. His uprightness is maintained by an invective against the canvas, the brushes, his arms, on account of their torpor.

So it is that two old adversaries – bodiless work of the mind, mindless work of the body – banish each other once more into opposite corners. With the latter he is able to acknowledge that the hours disappearing have as their guarantor a peculiar kind of change in the work. To think how it might be described invokes incomprehensible tongues of angels, of babbling, of nonsensical, musical utterance. But too often the actual mechanics of the craft are simply inadequate to the imaginings of his chair-bound state. Alterations to the work produce bewildering complications. He falls back into the sanctuary of his immobility. And then the gentle, unwitting work on the stain behind his head begins once more.

'IT'S FATIGUE THAT threatens.' The interviewer announces the idea as if it is a breakthrough. 'You fear being exiled to a world of banality, where the whole experience of looking at pictures would be reduced to a mere labour of viewing. That's the reason for your resolve not to go back and to look again at Rousseau's *Surprised! Tiger in a Tropical Storm*.'

The event his interviewee is describing is a prime case for sustained research, which makes it all the more strange that he should hold back rather than enquire further. Weather has seemed to appear inside the exhibition hall. It is unprecedented. There has been a palpable sensation of rain. That feeling has been produced purely by looking at a picture. In a room full of people a micro-climate has materialised. So striking has the experience been that, by his own account, he had become self-conscious, anxious that he might not be able to control his own response. The interviewee has testified to a facility; he could switch this unexpected sensation on and switch it off too with a gesture as simple as that of turning towards and turning away from the picture. Normally, feelings induced by a painting are spoken about as if they are either of the body or of the picture. Here they have become detached from both, freed to occupy another place.

'All this is to say, we're speaking about an anomaly,' the interviewer puts to him. 'What reason could there be for choosing not to pursue it?'

Increasingly, the journalist has been gesturing in a jerky and erratic way. His interviewee is not perturbed, is even a little amused, in his reply cautioning against the evident impatience. If the event recounted seems in some sense to have been an anomaly he has been inclined to treat it differently, almost inversely, as the precise normality of looking at pictures, that normality in a new form, in a distilled form. But let's not pursue that idea too quickly, he says. Certain observations and the questions that follow from them are better left to sit for a moment. That's the case even if — perhaps precisely when – they insist on attention.

We for our part agree with the point that has been made, to take sides with our esteemed colleague against his interviewer and to note that the charge of impatience may even be generous. There is something a little accusatory that creeps into his interviewing manner to indicate he has an agenda beyond the questions being asked. Our tendency to agree, while informed by the esteem in which we hold our colleague, is based first on our own experiences of a stepping back from unresolved issues and the value in doing so. Still, if we were given the opportunity, we would like to question our colleague at more length on the topic. In one case a choice can be made to leave ideas sitting; in another the pausing of thought is enforced by circumstances. It is likely that thought is not enabled equally in both instances.

For instance, we think back to the occasion we spotted the man by the railway arch. Our appreciation of what was taking place there was affected by an interruption we were obliged to accept. At the same time, while our thought on the topic was on hold, in retrospect is seems likely that such pauses of the conscious process are more complex than usually assumed. What we'd taken first for a mere rocking motion, as if the man was simply shifting his weight from one foot to the other, was in fact walking. As it happened we had an appointment and no time to stop and observe any longer. But finishing at the place of our appointment we returned the same way. Now the sight was all the more easy to interpret and we could see straight away what had taken us a little effort to work out before. Time had passed and yet the man was still there. Though he seemed to have progressed from his place it was by hardly any distance, so that if he had been trying to walk and yet to not move it would describe well his mode while we had been engaged in our business elsewhere.

So the man was walking but it would have to be said not getting very far. We made the remark. If we did not laugh we at least derived a little amusement from it, although felt anxious too on his account that circumstances should bring a person to spend a whole morning – indeed, half a working day – walking from one place by the railway arch to another where there is nothing. Now it occurs to us that if we felt some anxiety it was due also to the thought of our own steps in the normal course of things and how they are both less remarkable and in another way no different.

IT HAD OCCURRED TO us to think back on these events after looking at the way Martin was standing. He stood in a pose as if to walk. With the slight rocking motion of his body he moved his weight from one foot to the other. He held a rag in his hand and used it to wipe the handle of his brush, doing so intermittently with both hands then using one hand to make gestures accompanying his speaking. He gave the woman time to speak and listened in the way described. The woman expressed the idea that Martin's stack of panels was a thing worthy of attention. Quite apart from what each panel might show, the stack was a potent thing in its own right.

When Martin responded to her remark he did so to pause the conversation. The remark being a compliment, his reason was easy enough to read. Understanding the pause as an invitation, the woman spoke again. She offered her comment as she had before and did not elaborate. Most probably her intention was to develop the idea, only she had not worked out how to do so. All the same, it seemed to us, the words changed their meaning. By an increment her manner of speaking changed too. On account of her having taken encouragement to speak again she sounded a little more confident. Then as her meaning escaped her she was provoked to make the remark one more time, the words escaping her a little further still. And so what had been understood by all as a compliment was coming to appear less clearly so.

While it was a conversation troubled by confusion, looking at the whole it can be seen that to an extent and in different ways confusion was there purposefully. Allowing that it should be so is a way of instating the normal conditions of relaxed conversation. In the normal course of events we speak and we listen against a level of disorder that sits like a background. There is a noise of the competing present. The phrase is one that has been used by our notable friend. He too has pointed to a certain equivocation where questions of speaking and listening are concerned. In company one must work to draw out what's valuable in turbulent exchanges. If that work is perceived to be against one's intentions it is irksome. At the same time, if the imperatives of clarity and audibility are delivered, they are debilitating. Cacophony is preferable.

Certain phrases – this one in question may be a case – come to sit as gravitational centres around which others orientate in graceful orbits. If what our friend has told us of his childhood relies in complex ways on all he has said, this one phrase, along with a very few others like it, draws the eye. Furthermore it inspires a quick facility in us as we adopt it for our own purposes. It enters into our sub-vocal narratives and thus into our repertoire.

With the mere hint that the shop assistant has given us regarding events in the backroom, we are able to imagine. These two steps, the hint and the imagining, in being given to follow one another quickly, might miss the transformation of one into the other that happens by way of a legion of voices in the sub-vocal realm.

There is no one present except the shop assistant's young employee. The voices rise like steam, even in the silence, from a large pile of assorted books and papers that have slid to land in one heap on the floor. They are old stocks of books, pamphlets and magazines, unclassified items, details of suppliers' accounts, unsorted papers, documents in sequence losing their order as they fall. Thick bundles in plastic bags, sheets in sleeves – such things slide all the more effectively. These things have been put away badly. Over time an unwitting work has been done, many little acts of balancing achieved so that the cupboard door could be shut on an increasingly imminent collapse. It would have been better to ensure all items stored in order, papers secured in folders, lids of boxes replaced before other boxes were stacked on top of them, bundles of papers straightened and heavier things placed below lighter things.

From behind the door, before what's happening is in view, there is a sound of things sliding. The young employee thrusts his hand into the falling mass. It is too late and only contributes to the disorder. As the door swings fully open one or two last items fall. There is a pause. Then as if making itself more comfortable in the space between the cupboard and the open door the pile of stuff shifts a little. Turbulence, which has first been a quality of inanimate things, transfers. The young employee feels it as if his chest cavity too is a storage space in which things have been put. Then as suddenly as it began the turmoil settles and the disorder can be surveyed. A work of sorting previously not done must be done now, other tasks postponed while this problem is put right. All the same, if the job of sorting has been delayed before, can it not be again?

A distinction is needed between those on the one hand who insist that organisational tasks are completed in advance of work and those on the other who cannot work without an agitation of administrative business held at bay. What's at stake is the tendency of organs to shift their positions in sympathy with matters ensuing and the potential that such shifts hold. However, the opposition framed as between two kinds of worker fails to appreciate deeper identity in the two positions. Those who tidy obsessively, who cannot concentrate until everything is in place, in their compulsion, take the normal organisation of the chest cavity beyond itself. By instating an abnormal calm they evacuate that space. Then instating there an organisation of a different kind, their method is not opposite to others whose clutter transfers to become unusual corporeality.

Meanwhile, for his employer in the front shop, what had begun as normal dealings with a customer was quickly turning into something more complicated.

'AH YES,' THE SHOP ASSIS-
tant had said as he flicked
open the book, 'these
images *are* surprising.' A
remark of this kind should
come after the gesture of
looking. The judgement
would be of no use other-
wise. He was aware as he
spoke that something was wrong with the order. All
the same, thinking about it more closely, his gesture
with the book and his remark had in fact been given
in the way to be expected, with observation first and
judgement to follow. It was something else he'd got
wrong. The pause between observation and comment was too small. He had spoken to commend the
images in the book (and indirectly to commend his
customer for her choice) but had not left a sufficient
time between looking and speaking. The effect was
to make apparent that, actually, the judgement had
been there already in advance, that he had known
what he would say and that his looking was mere
performance.

These are our terms. When the shop assistant described it he had a different way of speaking.
He was inclined to say that the relationship
between gesture and words in this case was one of
a peculiar proximity, a zone in which orders
become unstable. In this way he accounted for his
uncertainty and his compulsion to describe these
things with increasing levels of accuracy.

It was important to the shop assistant to

impress on us the sequence in which these events took place. And not just his exchange with the woman as it manifested itself in words and gestures. Another sequence – that of his own realisation of what was taking place – was important to him too. Beyond that, he was concerned with the way these two impinged on one another. When he spoke to judge the pictures 'surprising' his words were somewhat implausible. That much was becoming clear to him. And he saw that there would be nothing gained by back-tracking. It was too late for repairs. More interestingly still, now the mistake had been made and his subterfuge exposed, he was seeing some virtue in allowing it to be so. The spectacle of his attempted artifice laid bare brought resolve where there had been none. Now he could say what he meant.

As it turned out his point was somewhat different. After he had finished telling us, we took the opportunity to contribute our own story. We did so without using names, all the better to render all that story might have to offer. The relationship between the characters mirrors his own with the woman. That said, it has not been our intention to suggest a direct equation nor to reduce one story to the other. Neither have we wanted to instruct him in any other way. Our aim has been simply to draw two different sequences of thought up next to one another and in that way to provoke an evaluation of their corresponding terms.

We told it like this. A writer writes at length on a story by another who has published only one short piece. The first writer aspires to be both commentator on the work of others and writer in his own right. He is ambitious. At the same time he is young and lacks experience. Though he is not sure where his own work is heading he knows enough that to give rein to his enthusiasm will be no betrayal. If there is maturity in his thought it is contained in this one insight.

Despite his ambition, through the innocence of his zeal, he leads those around him to think him wise beyond his years. In fact the aspiration that drives his endeavours is known to him only vaguely. He is seeking a work that orientates disciplines in a new way.

Other colleagues look on. Not least among them are one or two of his instructors and mentors who remark that their young protégé is impressive. If his work is at times unwieldy – if it does not yet reveal quite where its allegiances lie – still, in time, such things will become clear. So these older colleagues remember with some nostalgia the vitality of their own young hopes, how they too gave rein to their enthusiasms imagining disciplines reconfigured in accordance with the innovations of their work.

Being contemporaries and on the basis that one has written on the work of the other, the two young writers meet. They become friends. Then their working lives diverge. The first, who has fashioned his work as that simultaneously of writer and commentator, continues to work hard and with enthusiasm. He is prolific, achieves eminence, leaves comprehensive accounts of his intellectual journey in books, articles and interviews. In the meantime his friend who has written one short piece writes no more.

As the reputation of the first grows, those coming across the name and work of the second increase in number too. Other commentators look at the two and remark, saying that the less prolific hitches a ride on the work of his more esteemed friend. Not so, the contrary argument is put. The one focus of critical attention did not ask for it to be so. Furthermore, here is a writer whose output is genuinely notable and its true and hidden depths belie the apparent modesty of its size.

Thus, increasingly, the second finds his reputation growing more markedly than many other contemporaries who, without having been cited in the same way, have readerships restricted by comparison. He is a writer to be envied. They feel bitter encountering his name – and that only seems to cause it to appear even more frequently. Have they themselves not published consistently? Do they not deserve attention? It seems that a limited record of publishing is no disadvantage – on the contrary it can be the very guarantee of success. With every day their notable colleague does not write the notability of his one published work becomes more sure.

In due course disciplines orientate themselves anew. As they do so it is around this one short piece. Those who follow the unfolding lives of writers notice that in early commentary it had been predicted.

EACH PANEL THAT MARTIN was stacking with its face to the wall, quite apart from what it might show, was a thing in its own right worthy of attention. That's what the woman was saying. In finding the potency of his work in an unexpected place she was questioning his judgement, charging him that he may be looking the wrong way. Our gaze drawn to the stack of panels then returned to the panel on the stand, following what she said, to consider that as there is potency in many panels hidden, so there is impotency in one panel displayed; if many panels were to be displayed, impotency would be multiplied many times. That in itself might not be uninteresting, we thought, although without seeing it, it would be difficult to imagine how.

As it was repeated the woman's remark moved by increments towards criticism. With its increasing evidence we have been inclined to attribute the analysis more clearly to her. But on reflection was it not Martin who invoked it first? Was the woman's intervention not merely to elaborate what he had given in his description of a day's work? Now we wonder, if she had been allowed to speak once more would her remark have become by another increment more like the criticism it was tending towards? Or would her meaning have deviated in some other way? As it was, the conversation moved on and we are unable to remember what else was said.

To recall these things to the extent we have managed has required some strategy. We have put decoys in place, thought at a tangent, distracted ourselves, invented procedures. It has been a matter of summoning up the ambiance of a room, the light, the white sky, the constellation of bodies present. Odd memories of irrelevancies persisting with peculiar vividness for reasons unknown have been found important. Our acquaintances have spoken indirectly, doing so for reasons of their own. Meanwhile others have imbued their remarks with concision and clear visibility to provoke on our part a different kind of thought. Well-phrased words have been given to appear again as if of their own accord. They have brought with them related phrases that gravitate in orbits. That way too whole worlds have emerged out of thought's dark background.

We think again of the surprises described in exhibition halls, of the child captivated by the type-setter's emblem. If we come back to these thoughts it is because our friends and colleagues have done so, recounting events with a sense of wonder – with barely a jot of self-regard – to tell how things worthy of attention have been spotted even in the midst of a day's excitements, banalities and anxieties; even through the noise of the competing present. The wonder is that such events remain available. When they do it is because procedures have been found to make it possible. Such procedures are not the tools of comprehension – or if they are, the understanding they bring is deferred and divided, made a collegiate achievement, a work of association, a crowning of friendship.

Think of the book-seller. He has revealed to us how he observes his customers. Perhaps they buy a book, perhaps not. In any event, often they leave without making eye-contact. He feels sympathy with these customers especially, whose time spent in the shop goes far beyond normal browsing. Through their evident perplexity they inspire respect more than any well-socialised patrons who know how to find what they want and buy it without delay. In the company of the former he begins to appreciate something of his own day and the work he engages in while in other respects he would seem to be doing nothing.

It is in many respects odd, he concedes, that he should sit in the proximity of the resources he has stacked on his shelves. How can he resist delving into these volumes? He could become the self-educated master of their contents. As things are, he is happy simply to be in their proximity. Maybe on the odd occasion – when the shop is empty in the evening – he feels the threat of their distilled resource. The shelves seem taller, the aisles between them narrower. The strip-lighting takes on a caustic quality and in the silence he is exposed. That said, such anxieties are fleeting and well managed by his resolve to sit and to be satisfied with the host of voices animating his thoughts.

Now he understands. In another way he is master of his stock – if not of their content then of their spines. Like a spider, his work is to wait. Just as some insects enlist the labours of other species, he will allow his attention to the books to be limited to the choices made by others, who walk to the till and pass a volume into his hands as if giving themselves. Is he delegating risk? Certainly. More than a few will leave with their thoughts addled by the reading and the looking in which they have indulged without sufficient caution. But his work involves a moment of giving too. With a word or gesture he will indicate the rarity of his customer's find. As the customer's doubts evaporate she will leave with renewed vigour to put her purchase to use. And it will be unclear whether she is an element in his operation, or he in hers.

IN DUE COURSE WE LEFT
Martin and the woman
and made our exit the way
we had come. There are
swing doors leading to
the stairwell and a set at
the bottom through which
one might turn right or
left. To the right, several
doors line the corridor on either side with two
doors at the end. There are no windows. The corridor is fitted with strip-lights. These are usually
not switched on, although even when they are
the illumination is barely sufficient. Occasionally,
when one or other of the doors to a room is open,
light from the windows spills out to illuminate
the corridor but it happens rarely. If you wish you
can pause for a moment without fear of being disturbed. To the left, another set of swing doors
gives access to the hall. With its tall windows the
hall is warm. Here the sun shines in directly, often
harshly. On sunny days, even then it may be felt
that a view out cannot be had. The windows are
high, above eye level and protected by grills on the
outside, which both obstruct looking and forbid
the cleaning of the windows so that dirt contributes to their opacity. A person standing in
the hall and hoping to look out is denied what
may have been visible otherwise – the white sky,
trees, roofs of buildings nearby.

Sounds of footfalls can be heard in the echoey
stairwell. The main door to the street is opened then

closed. Walk over to the window. Stand up on tip-toes. Get up close to the glass and see who's leaving. It is a surprise to notice again how quickly the one departing establishes distance while a person inside has managed no more than a few paces across the room. Already disappearing, he is a man with un-kempt appearance. It is Rousseau.

Up until just a moment ago his work was going well. He was inspired, was making changes to the picture. The new vitality of the work surprised him. Then his buoyant feeling of progress began to decline. In a hurry he opted to leave, to distract him-self with other things.

Though he is seen now departing and seems to be doing so with resolve, as he made to open the main door a doubt crossed his mind. Perhaps this departure was premature. With a hand on the door-knob his options appeared two-fold – either leave as planned or turn and go back up the stairs. If there had been someone there to witness, that witness would have seen Rousseau confound the options. For an instant his body was held in the doorway.

While the common phrase states it of a person that *he did not know if he was coming or going* its familiarity elides the material, gestural reality of indecision. A person attuned to such a thing sees it even as it diminishes. What they have seen can be relayed – written or recounted – expanded to the inverse proportion.

Rousseau has left the building. He has made his way to the corner. Now he can go no further. Neither can he find a reason to retrace his steps.

His hair is long, coarse, bleached by the sun. He squints against the light. The dust has worked its way into his clothing. His body is dry with the city's dust. He stands on the narrow strip of pavement on the road side of an iron barrier put up to usher pedestrians to a safer crossing place. He grips the railing with both hands. Carriages pass behind. Beyond the barrier, concrete expanses of the bus terminus stretch in every direction. A diagonal line here would lead him onto the main street. He can barely recall why he might have set out this way. At the same time the idea of going back induces in his limbs such a crystalline stiffness that he can do nothing but stand where he finds himself, here on the road side of the barrier in the harsh daylight.

It is clear enough that an ecology of the painter's work relies in complex ways on his disequilibrium. For the character in the story, no resolution will be granted. At the cost of his distress his movements are shown to be more intelligent than he knows. Rousseau is no longer in the proximity of his picture. He is unable even to think about it clearly. And yet he has not stopped working. What the story says obliquely, the commentator puts more directly. In front of *Surprised! Tiger in a Tropical Storm*, surprising things take place. They come to interrupt the normal business of looking at the picture.

What is the normal business of looking at a picture?

Let's say it's that we look and that we look away.

STEPPING THROUGH THE
swing doors we turned
right into the dark portion
where the corridor comes
to an end. We stopped for
a moment. The cool air
seemed to fit with the
darkness and with the
likelihood that we would
not be disturbed. We did not stop for long, only
to better appreciate the coolness, the dimness
of the space and its seclusion, qualities which
seemed in consort as if having sought each
other's company. We came momentarily to a standstill. We did so to register that here, where it is
dark, it is cool and at the same time quiet. On
reflection, that standstill was little more than two feet
brought together to interrupt the course of walking,
the darkness of the corridor, the coolness and the
seclusion being registered thus for their consort.
Then again, perhaps the impression of us having
interrupted our walking was merely that, an
impression, when in fact there was no interruption, only dim light, cool air and the feeling of
solitude, these three together.

So we have noted the qualities of the place
as we walked and as we listened. There was barely
any sound but we listened before walking forward
into the darkest portion towards the two doors at
the end of the corridor and then towards our own
door. Opening it, as we had anticipated, we were met
by a great flood of light. Then that light no doubt

flooded the corridor behind us. Only we did not look round to see because we were already involved in what the bright-illuminated space of our own room presented.

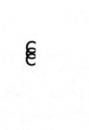

VIT HOPLEY

Wednesday Afternoon

Wednesday Afternoon is a collection of prose that introduces awkward perspectives on all manner of things: a house taken on an arduous journey across a frozen lake, a puff of dust released from yesterday's socks, a death in a basement, a gathering of strangers. Vit Hopley pays attention to every detail. She writes on sitting, standing and lying down, but most significantly she creates a stillness that is almost photographic.

'Wednesday Afternoon *has shown words anew. It's very much like fresh rain and fresh air.*'
PHILIPPA BREWSTER

MICHAEL SCHWAB

Paris

Michael Schwab is curious about trees in Paris. The most unnatural thing about a tree in a city is the place where it is planted. A tree in a city does not grow; it is planted. *Paris* lets you explore trees in Paris while it breaches narrow definitions of photography.

'*So you think you know Paris, but if you take Michael Schwab as your guide you will find yourself in a truly inventive space between photography and drawing. You will be delightfully transported to spaces and places of the imagination, with some very particular trees to hold on to for reality. This is indeed Paris from another perspective.*'

VANESSA JACKSON

JASPAR JOSEPH-LESTER

Revisiting the Bonaventure Hotel

This book is a photo-essay that describes the life of a building through a range of film stills, photographic images and written citations. With *Revisiting the Bonaventure Hotel* we wander between references to Fredric Jameson, John Portman and Arnold Schwarzenegger as we view a world through different perspectives: vertical, horizontal and rotating. This is a story about the image.

'I loved it. Looks like a Chris Marker book, so glamorous.'

CHRIS KRAUS

HAYLEY NEWMAN

Common

Through fact and fiction, questions and answers, writings from the heart and writing from the street, *Common* chronicles one day of a Self-Appointed Artist-in-Residence in the City of London. Performances occur and reoccur as this book takes us to crashes in global markets, turbulence in the Euro-zone, riots on hot summer nights and the most extraordinary imaginings.

'The financial sector in the City of London is often viewed as an impermeable, inaccessible block, and that perception is what gives it a lot of its power. In Common, *Hayley Newman has subverted that, opening the City up through richly imaginative stories that are at once creative examples of how to play with the space, and empowering political actions. I hope this book will inspire others to embark on similar transformative adventures.'*

BRETT SCOTT

ANNE TALLENTIRE

Object of a Life

Oscillating between depiction and description, *Object of a Life* addresses the question: How are we to speak of common things? Making an inventory of things that come to hand in the course of daily life, playing with ideas of contradiction, categorisation, improbability and speculation, this book offers an articulation of the space produced between language and drawing.

'In Object of a Life *Anne Tallentire extends her enquiry past the objects of everyday life to ruminate on the space in between and around the objects' relationship to their sites of activity including the domestic, the studio and the street. Like all good artists' writing, this book calls upon us to think differently...'*

LISA PANTING

JAKI IRVINE

Days of Surrender

In 1916, when Padraic Pearse, Irish republican and leader of the 'Easter Rising', decided to surrender, he asked midwife Elizabeth O'Farrell to make the perilous walk to deliver his message to the British army. Setting off down a Dublin street where some of the dead still held white flags in their hands, Elizabeth O'Farrell was watched from the door by Julia Grenan, referred to in documents as her 'friend and lifelong companion.' This is the story of those days.

Copy Press is committed to bringing readers and writers together and invites you to join its Reader's Union – please visit www.copypress.co.uk